Level 3 is ideal for ___
reading confidence and ___
to read longer stories v ___

Special features:

Wider
vocabulary,
reinforced
through
repetition

Once, there was a poor boy called Aladdin.

One day a man said to him, "I am your uncle. I will help you."

He was not really Aladdin's uncle, he was a magician.

Detailed
pictures
for added
interest and
discussion

Longer
sentences

"I will make you very rich," the magician said.

He made a fire and black smoke came up. Then Aladdin saw a stone with a handle on it.

Simple story
structure

Educational Consultant: Geraldine Taylor
Book Banding Consultant: Kate Ruttle

A catalogue record for this book is available from the British Library

Published by Ladybird Books Ltd
80 Strand, London, WC2R 0RL
A Penguin Company

002
© LADYBIRD BOOKS LTD MMXIV.
Ladybird, Read It Yourself and the Ladybird Logo are registered or
unregistered trademarks of Ladybird Books Limited.

ISBN: 978-0-72328-082-8

Printed in China

Aladdin

Retold by Jillian Powell
Illustrated by Livia Coloji

Once, there was a poor boy
called Aladdin.

One day a man said to him, "I am
your uncle. I will help you."

He was not really Aladdin's uncle,
he was a magician.

7

"I will make you very rich,"
the magician said.

He made a fire and black smoke
came up. Then Aladdin saw
a stone with a handle on it.

"Pull that handle," said the magician. The stone came up and Aladdin could see a black well.

"If you want to be rich, go down there," the magician said. "You will see a lamp. Bring it back to me. This ring will help you."

12

13

Aladdin left the magician and went down to the bottom of the well.

At the bottom of the well was a cave. There, he saw a garden.

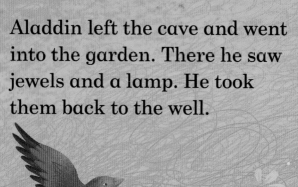

Aladdin left the cave and went
into the garden. There he saw
jewels and a lamp. He took
them back to the well.

At the well, the magician said,
"Give mc the lamp!"

"Help me out first," said Aladdin.

The magician was so angry that
he put the stone back on the well
and Aladdin could not get out.

18

Aladdin was in the garden
for three days.

Poor Aladdin was cold. He rubbed
his hands. This rubbed the ring, too.

A genie appeared in a puff of smoke!
"I am the Genie of the Ring,"
he said. "What is your wish?"

"I wish to go home!"
Aladdin said.

21

He was back home at once.

Aladdin said, "I must have some dinner, so I will sell this lamp."

"This lamp looks so old," his mother said. She rubbed it to make it look new.

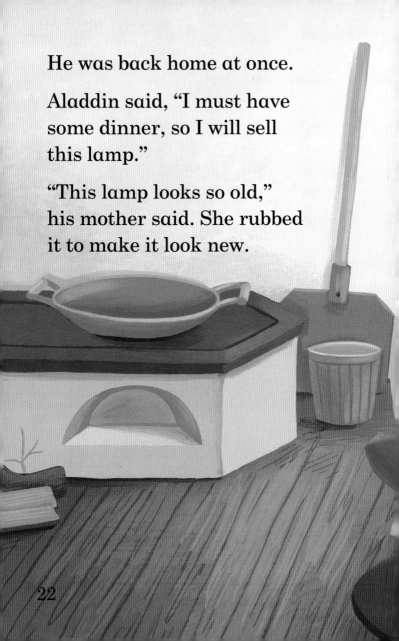

There was a puff of smoke,
and another genie appeared.
"What is your wish?" said the
Genie of the Lamp.

"I wish for some dinner!"
Aladdin said.

At once, they had dinner.

24

Time went by. Aladdin was now a
rich man. Every time he rubbed
the lamp, the genie came to him.

One day, Aladdin saw a princess
go by and he fell in love with her.

27

"I want to marry that princess!" said Aladdin.

"We must go to see the king," his mother said.

They gave the king the jewels Aladdin had taken from the garden. The king said Aladdin could marry the princess.

Aladdin rubbed the lamp.
"Genie, I wish for a really big
house," he said.

Aladdin married the princess
and they lived in the big house.

Time went by. One day, the magician came back. He saw Aladdin was rich.

"The magic lamp has made him rich," he said. "I must have it!"

When Aladdin was away, the magician went to see the princess. "I will give you a new lamp if you give me that old one," he said.

"A new lamp for Aladdin!" the princess said. She gave the magician Aladdin's old lamp.

The magician rubbed the lamp. "Genie, make Aladdin's house go away," he said.

The house and the princess disappeared.

The king was very angry. "Aladdin!" he said, "Get the princess back!"

Aladdin rubbed the magic ring on his hand. "Genie of the Ring, take me to the princess," he said.

At once he was with the princess.

"The old lamp is magic!" Aladdin said to the princess, "we must get it back."

39

So that night they gave
the magician dinner.

"Put this in his dinner,"
Aladdin said to the princess.

The magician ate his dinner and
disappeared in a puff of smoke.

Aladdin rubbed the lamp.
"Genie, take us home!"
he said.

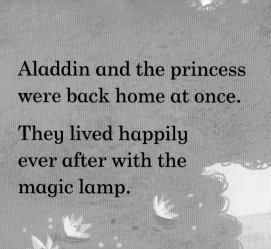

Aladdin and the princess
were back home at once.

They lived happily
ever after with the
magic lamp.

How much do you remember about the story of Aladdin? Answer these questions and find out!

- Who does the magician pretend to be?

- What happens when Aladdin rubs the ring?

- What is magical about Aladdin's lamp?

- Who does Aladdin fall in love with?

- What makes the magician disappear?